C000137698

Laughter's for Afters

Silvey-Jex

ℛℛ

RAVETTE PUBLISHING

First published by Ravette Publishing 2009.

Ravette Publishing Limited
PO Box 876
Horsham
West Sussex RH12 9GH

ISBN: 978-1-84161-327-7

RIGHT-NO STARTERS OR MAINS, WE'LL HAVE 3 HOT CHOCOLATE SOUFFLES, 3 CHOCOLATE FUDGE CAKES, 3 CHOCOLATE ROULADES, 3 CHOCOLATE PROFITEROLES, THEN 3 CHOCOLATE MOUSSE AND A LARGE 'DEATH BY CHOCOLATE' TO SHARE THANKYOU
SJ

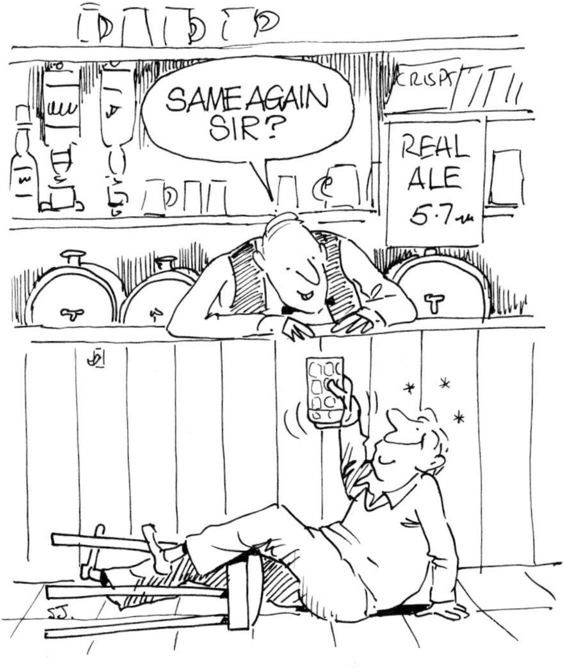
SAME AGAIN SIR?
CRISPS
REAL ALE

SO, YOU DIDN'T LIKE THE STARTER OR THE MAIN COURSE OR THE SWEET OR THE CHEESE OR THE COFFEE AND NOW, I UNDERSTAND, THE BILL ISN'T TO YOUR LIKING
BILL
SJ